This book belongs to

_____

_____

This edition published by Parragon Books Ltd in 2014

Parragon Books Ltd
Chartist House
15–17 Trim Street
Bath BA1 1HA, UK
www.parragon.com

ISBN 978-1-4723-8196-5

Printed in China

Disney · PIXAR MOVIE COLLECTION
A SPECIAL DISNEY STORYBOOK SERIES

Finding Nemo

Bath · New York · Cologne · Melbourne · Delhi
Hong Kong · Shenzhen · Singapore · Amsterdam

At the edge of the Great Barrier Reef, a mother and father clownfish watched over their eggs that were about to hatch. "We still have to name them," Coral told her husband, Marlin. She wanted to call one of them, Nemo.

Suddenly, a barracuda
attacked and knocked Marlin
out cold! He awoke to discover
that one tiny injured egg was all
that was left of his family.

"I promise I will never let anything
happen to you ... Nemo," Marlin said.

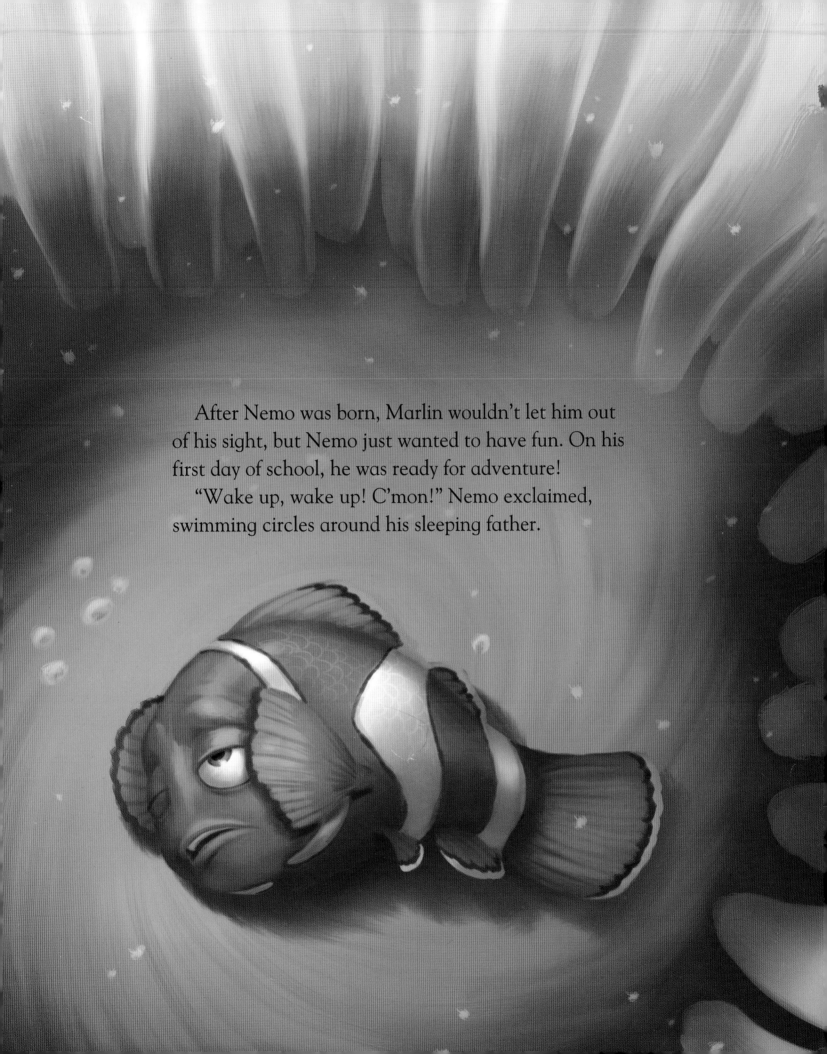

After Nemo was born, Marlin wouldn't let him out of his sight, but Nemo just wanted to have fun. On his first day of school, he was ready for adventure!

"Wake up, wake up! C'mon!" Nemo exclaimed, swimming circles around his sleeping father.

As they swam to school together, Marlin kept reminding Nemo to hold his fin. After all, the ocean was a dangerous place!

Nemo met up with his class. The teacher, Mr Ray, assured Marlin that Nemo would be safe.

At the Drop-off, Nemo swam away with his new friends, Tad the butterfly fish, Sheldon the seahorse and Pearl the octopus. They dared each other to swim up to a dive boat and touch it.

But then, Mr Ray found them – and so did Marlin!

Marlin was angry at Nemo. "You think you can just do these things, but you can't!" he declared.

Nemo wanted to prove his dad wrong, so he swam right up to the boat and hit it with his fin!

Marlin told Nemo to swim back immediately. But suddenly a diver appeared!

"Daddy! Help me!" Nemo shouted.

Marlin started to swim towards his son, but at that moment, a second diver took a photograph and Marlin was blinded by the flash. In the meantime, the first diver had caught Nemo in a net. Marlin was too late!

Marlin raced to the surface as the
divers sped away. A scuba mask flew
overboard and dropped into the ocean,
then the boat disappeared.
"Nemo!" Marlin cried.

Marlin rushed to get help. "Has anybody seen a boat?" he cried. He soon collided with a blue fish named Dory. She told him she had seen a boat. "Follow me!" she said.

Marlin didn't know it, but Dory had a very bad memory. After just a few seconds, she couldn't even remember why Marlin was following her! "Will you quit it?" she asked.

Confused, Marlin turned to swim away …

... and came face to face with a great white shark!

The shark, whose name was Bruce, told Marlin and Dory he just wanted to be friends. Marlin was sure it was a trap!

Bruce took them to a sunken submarine to meet his buddies, Anchor and Chum. The sharks were trying to become vegetarians. They chanted, "Fish are friends, not food!"

Just then, Marlin spotted the mask that had fallen off the divers' boat! He wondered if the writing on the strap might be a clue to help him find Nemo.

Dory wanted to ask the sharks if they could read it, but the strap snapped and made her nose bleed. The scent of blood tempted Bruce and he suddenly wanted to eat Dory after all!

Marlin and Dory escaped through a field of
sea mines. Bruce accidentally set one off and the
explosion that followed rocked the entire ocean.
Marlin and Dory took cover inside the mask!

Meanwhile, Nemo was dropped into strange waters that had plastic plants and invisible walls. A group of fish soon came out of hiding. Bubbles, Peach, Jacques, Bloat, Deb and Gurgle were thrilled to meet a fish from the open sea. Nemo learned that he was in a fish tank in a dentist's office.

Soon after, Nigel the pelican stopped by for a visit. Nigel greeted
Nemo kindly, but was soon shooed away by the dentist, Dr Sherman.
The fish overheard Dr Sherman saying that Nemo was going
to be a present for his niece, Darla. The others warned Nemo that
Darla wasn't very nice to fish! Nemo was worried.

That night, the group's leader,
Gill, made Nemo an official
member of their tank gang.
Gill announced, "From this
moment on, you will be known
as 'Shark Bait'."

Next, Gill revealed that he had an escape plan. First, Nemo would break the tank's water filter. That would force the dentist to remove them all and place them in plastic bags while he cleaned the tank. Then all they'd have to do was roll out of the window to freedom!

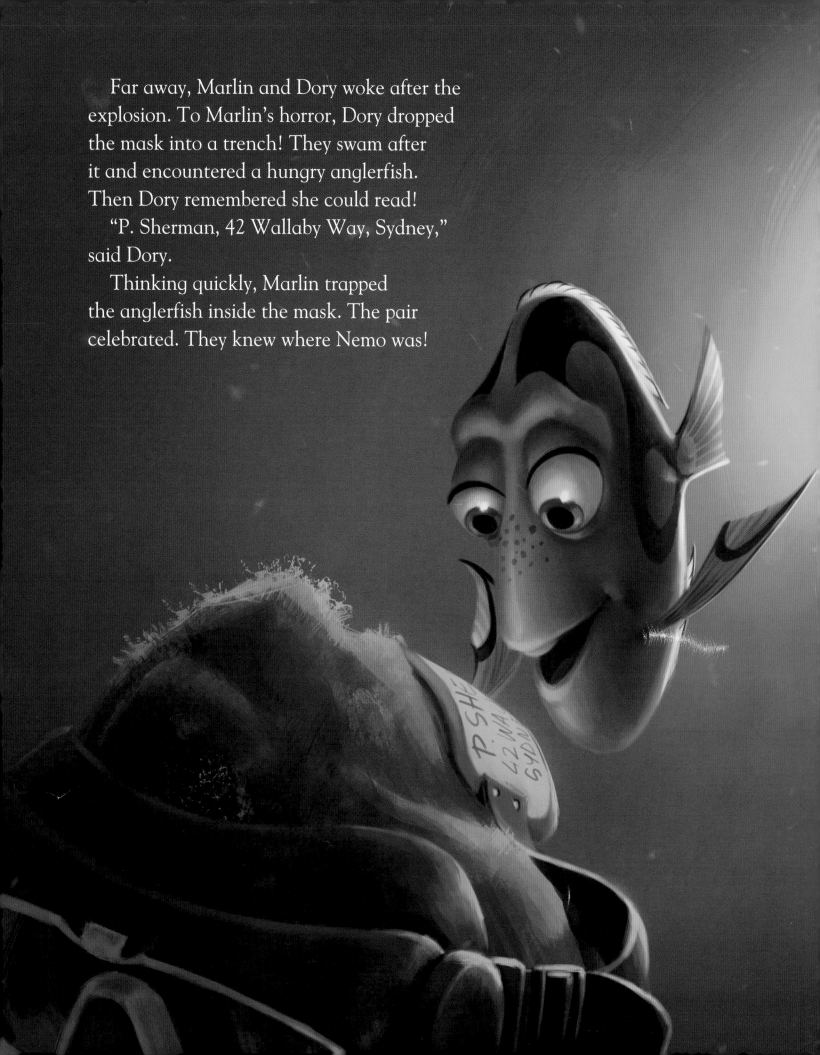

Far away, Marlin and Dory woke after the explosion. To Marlin's horror, Dory dropped the mask into a trench! They swam after it and encountered a hungry anglerfish. Then Dory remembered she could read!

"P. Sherman, 42 Wallaby Way, Sydney," said Dory.

Thinking quickly, Marlin trapped the anglerfish inside the mask. The pair celebrated. They knew where Nemo was!

Marlin and Dory asked a school of moonfish if they knew how to get to Sydney.

"Follow the East Australian Current," they said. Then they gave Dory a warning. "When you come to a trench, swim through it, not over it."

When the pair reached the trench, Marlin insisted that they swim
over it, despite what the moonfish had said. He thought it would be safer.
But soon they were surrounded by jellyfish! They tried to bounce on
the tops of the jellyfish to avoid the stinging tentacles, but by the time
they reached the safety of the open sea, they had been stung over and
over again. Marlin helped Dory to safety, then they both passed out.

Back in the tank, Gill caught Nemo looking at his damaged fin. "My first escape," he said. He told Nemo he had tried to jump into the toilet. "All drains lead to the ocean, kid," said Gill.

Soon, the first phase of the escape plan was in motion. Nemo swam into the filter tube and jammed a pebble inside, but it didn't hold. As Nemo swam back down the plastic tube, he began to be sucked back towards the filter's deadly blades!

The gang quickly used a plastic plant to pull
Nemo out just in time!
    Gill felt terrible. Not only had his escape plan
failed, but he had put Nemo's life in danger.

Meanwhile, some sea turtles had rescued
Marlin and Dory.

"Takin' on the jellies – awesome!" exclaimed
Crush, a surfer turtle.

Dory played hide-and-seek with some
baby turtles, including Crush's son, Squirt.
Crush encouraged his children to be
adventurous. He thought it taught
them important lessons. Marlin
wondered if he had been too
protective of Nemo.

The baby turtles had lots of questions for Marlin. He told them all about his search for Nemo. Soon the story was being passed across the ocean from turtle to fish to lobster to swordfish to dolphin to pelican to ... Nigel!

"Your dad's been fighting the entire ocean looking for you," Nigel told Nemo.

"My father?" Nemo asked. "Really?"

Nigel nodded his head. "Word is, he's headed this way to Sydney."

Nemo was inspired by his dad's bravery. To his
friends' horror, Nemo darted into the filter again.
But this time he successfully jammed it! All the
fish cheered!

Before long, the Tank Gang was swimming in slimy,
green water, but they couldn't have been happier!
Dr Sherman was going to have to clean
the tank before Darla arrived.

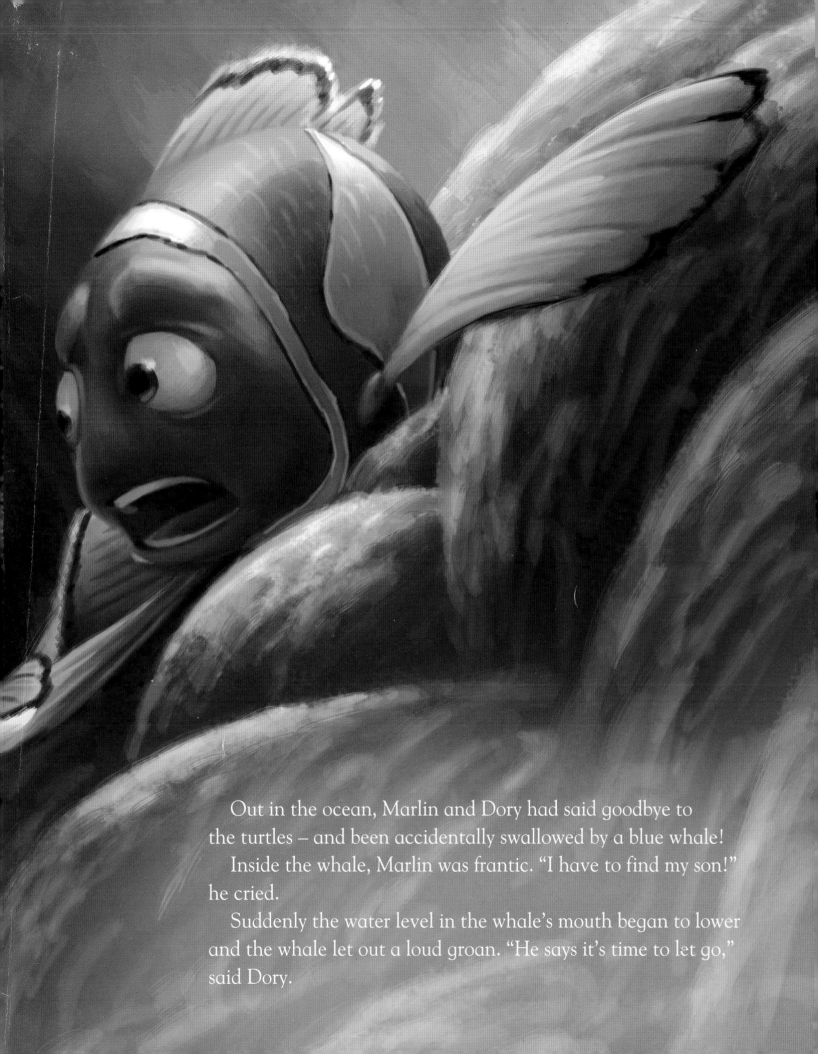

Out in the ocean, Marlin and Dory had said goodbye to
the turtles – and been accidentally swallowed by a blue whale!
Inside the whale, Marlin was frantic. "I have to find my son!"
he cried.
Suddenly the water level in the whale's mouth began to lower
and the whale let out a loud groan. "He says it's time to let go,"
said Dory.

For once, Marlin did as he was told. Suddenly, the whale spouted out the two fish right into Sydney Harbour! The pai searched for the divers' boat, but couldn't find it.

That same morning, Nemo and his friends woke up to a clean tank. The dentist had installed a brand-new filter while they were sleeping! "The escape plan is ruined!" Bloat cried.

Just then, Dr Sherman walked through the door. The dentist fished Nemo out with a net and plopped him in a plastic bag. Nemo went belly-up. His friends were shocked. "He's dead!" exclaimed Bloat.

Little did they know that Nemo was faking it!

Meanwhile, Marlin and Dory had been scooped up by a hungry pelican and dropped onto the dock. Luckily, Nigel was nearby. He heard Marlin exclaim, "I've gotta find my son, Nemo!"

Nigel instantly knew who Marlin was and wanted to help him. "Hop inside my mouth if you want to live!" Nigel whispered.

Nigel snatched up Marlin and Dory,
filled his beak with water and took off.
The hungry seagulls followed, but Nigel
played a trick on them. The seagulls
flew right into a sail!

Back at the dentist's office, Darla burst into the room, wanting her new fish. Dr Sherman thought Nemo was dead, so he hid him behind his back. Nemo winked at his friends. His plan was working!

Just then, Nigel flew through the window with
Marlin and Dory. In shock, the dentist dropped Nemo
onto a tray. Marlin gasped – he saw Nemo in the bag
and thought he was dead.

Darla picked up Nemo's bag and shook it. The Tank Gang knew they had to do something. They launched Gill out of the fish tank's bubble volcano and onto Darla's head! She screamed and threw the bag up into the air. When it landed on the tray, Nemo came tumbling out!

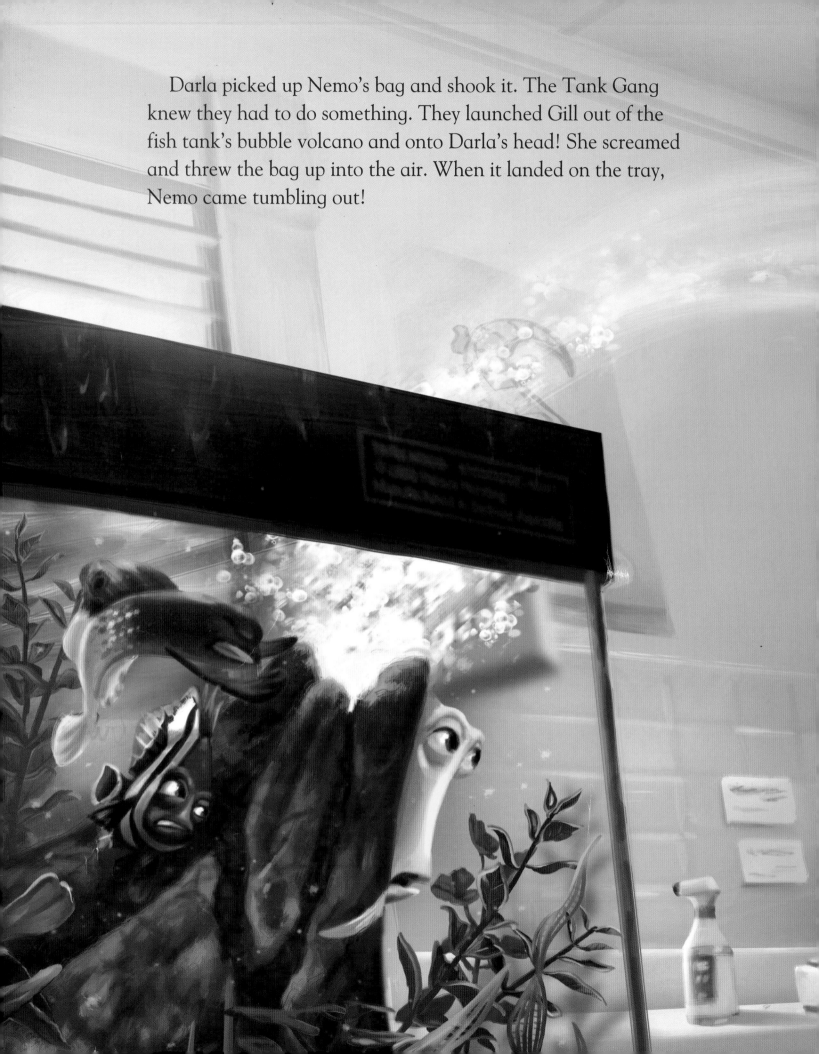

Gill flipped himself onto the tray beside Nemo.
"Tell your dad I said 'hi'," he said. Then Gill smacked
his tail on a dental mirror, catapulting Nemo over Darla's
waiting hands and into the sink. The little fish escaped
down the drain!

Back in the harbour, Nigel dropped Dory and Marlin into the sea. Marlin was heartbroken. He thanked Dory for her help and sadly said goodbye.

Dory would miss Marlin terribly. He had become like family to her.

Meanwhile, Nemo rode the rapids through a water treatment plant. When he finally came out, he was greeted by two hungry crabs.

Nemo quickly swam away. He had no idea that his dad was so near by!

Nemo soon met Dory. At first she had no memory of who he was. When she finally did remember, Dory knew she had to reunite Nemo with his dad straight away!

The crabs told her that Marlin had gone to the fishing grounds.

Dory and Nemo finally found Marlin! But there was no time to celebrate. A net swept up Dory along with a huge school of fish!

Nemo bravely plunged into the net and told the fish to swim downwards. His plan worked – the net broke open and all the fish escaped!

Marlin found Nemo pinned beneath the heavy net.
To his enormous relief, his son's eyes fluttered open.
Nemo was going to be all right.

Marlin finally realized that even though Nemo was
a little fish, he was capable of doing very big things!

A few weeks later, Marlin and all his new
friends showed up at Nemo's school. Nemo gave
Marlin a big hug before heading off with his class.
It was time for a new adventure!

Meanwhile, the Tank Gang had finally managed to break the new filter, forcing Dr Sherman to clean the tank. They had made their daring escape and were now floating in Sydney Harbour!

There was just one problem – how were they going to get out of those bags!